Constructing narratives

Book 2

Characters
- Drawing characters
- Describing characters
- Character passports
- Creating characters

Dialogue
- Effective dialogue
- Dialogue rules
- Designing dialogue
- Developing dialogue

Genres and settings
- Story genres
- Story settings
- Using the senses
- Creating a scene

Planning
- Story plans
- Making an ideas pack
- The story path
- Path of ideas

Drafting
- Beginning a story
- Continuing a story
- Ending a story
- Cover it

Revising
- Practising revising
- Revising the beginning
- Revising the middle
- Revising the end

Presenting
- Author profile
- Introducing you
- Story blurbs
- Introducing your story

Susie Brown

Published by Prim-Ed Publishing

0797C

CONSTRUCTING NARRATIVES
(Book 2)

Published by Prim-Ed Publishing 2006
Reprinted under licence by
Prim-Ed Publishing 2006
Copyright© Susie Brown 2005
ISBN 1 84654 033 X
PR–0797

Additional titles available in this series:
CONSTRUCTING NARRATIVES *(Book 1)*
CONSTRUCTING NARRATIVES *(Book 3)*

Republic of Ireland: Bosheen, New Ross, Co. Wexford, Ireland   Email: sales@prim-ed.com

Internet websites

In some cases, websites or specific URLs may be recommended. While these are checked and rechecked at the time of publication, the publisher has no control over any subsequent changes which may be made to webpages. It is *strongly* recommended that the class teacher checks *all* URLs before allowing pupils to access them.

View all pages online

http://www.prim-ed.com

Foreword

Constructing narratives is a series of three books that have been designed to give pupils the skills to confidently write effective creative stories. The pupils are introduced to the writing process through activities that follow a step-by-step approach and progressively build upon the skills being learnt. Pupils plan, draft, revise and present creative stories that not only contain a beginning, middle and end, but have colourful characters, descriptive settings and effective dialogue.

Other titles in this series are:

- **Constructing narratives** Book 1
- **Constructing narratives** Book 3

Contents

Teachers notes

Constructing narratives is a series of three books designed to lead pupils through the process of creative writing. Each book is divided into seven sections that address different components of the writing process. These are:

- characters
- dialogue
- genres and settings
- planning
- drafting
- revising
- presenting

Each section contains four activities. The activities are accompanied by detailed teachers notes that provide examples and assessment checklists focusing on the skills being addressed. As each activity builds upon the skills learnt in the previous lesson, it is suggested that the worksheets be introduced in order, rather than at random. Each worksheet is designed to be completed in one lesson.

The structure of each book in the series is identical, with the activities having the same headings and main focus. This feature allows pupils with different ability levels to be working on the same activity in the one classroom. The activities increase in difficulty throughout the levels of the books. This allows for easy use within a multi-ability classroom.

Pupils will develop their understanding of the 'beginning', 'middle' and 'end' of a story and learn the requirements of each. Further activities allow pupils to focus on developing interesting characters, descriptive settings and dialogue that includes thoughts and actions.

Pupils will revise and polish their writing in stages—focusing on spelling and punctuation, correctly written dialogue and interesting text.

The activities lead pupils to create stories that have a plot and structure, as well as situations that are resolved by the final paragraph.

Note re punctuation: The punctuation used in this publication conforms to the rules set out in *Style manual for authors, editors and printers*, sixth edition, Wiley and Sons.

Teacher pages

Each pupil page is supported by a teachers page which provides the following information.

Objective(s) *provides the focus of the lesson.*

Teacher information *provides suggestions for teaching the lesson. Specific examples and answers are included where appropriate.*

Additional activities *are suggestions to further develop the focus of the activity. They may also be used as extension activities for fast-finishing pupils.*

The **Assessment checklist** *provides a list of specific skills that should be demonstrated by the pupils. These can be used for either anecdotal or written assessment records.*

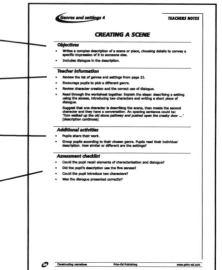

Pupil pages

Specific instructions are provided and space given for written responses.

Some worksheets allow for pupils to illustrate their ideas.

Where appropriate, handy hints and reminders are given to help pupils complete the activity.

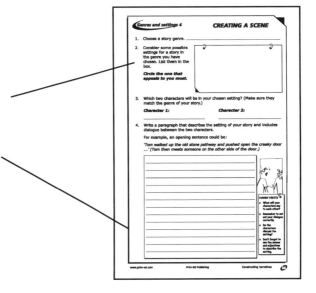

The generic pages provide the opportunity for each pupil to evaluate his/her efforts and gain a sense of achievement by earning a certificate of completion once his/her stories have been presented.

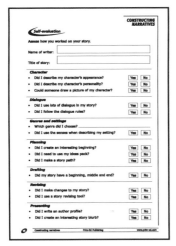

The **Self-evaluation** worksheet is to be given to the pupils once their stories are completed. Pupils may need to look back at their work and at their finished story to complete the evaluation. Remind them that all writers have areas that need improving and that it is important to be honest. Teachers can use this evaluation for assessment and reporting purposes.

This certificate can be presented to pupils who have satisfactorily completed the worksheets to the best of their ability. Teachers may wish to organise an assembly where pupils read their completed stories and are presented with the certificates.

Self-evaluation

Assess how you worked on your story. Read and answer each of the questions. Include a comment about your story at the bottom of this sheet.

Name of writer: [   ]   Title of story: [   ]

Character

- Did I create a detailed description of my main character?   Yes   No

- Did I describe my character's personality, background and hobbies?   Yes   No

Dialogue

- Did I use dialogue in my story?   Yes   No

- Did I follow the dialogue rules?   Yes   No

Genres and settings

- Which genre did I choose? _____

- Did I use the senses when describing my setting?   Yes   No

Planning

- Did I create an interesting beginning with a two-sentence hook?   Yes   No

- Did I need to use my ideas pack?   Yes   No

- Did I create a detailed story path?   Yes   No

Drafting

- Did my story have a beginning, middle and end?   Yes   No

- My story was _____ words long.

Revising

- Did I correct spelling and punctuation errors in my story?   Yes   No

Presenting

- Did I write an author profile?   Yes   No

- Did I create an interesting story blurb?   Yes   No

My opinion of my story: _____

CREATIVE WRITING CERTIFICATE

This is to certify that

Has successfully completed writing exercises on the following topics:

- Characters

- Dialogue

- Genres and settings

- Planning

- Drafting

- Revising

- Presenting

and has written an interesting and well-structured story titled

---

Well done!

Signed: ....

Date: ....

CONSTRUCTING NARRATIVES

The structure of each book in the series is identical, with the activities having the same headings and main focus. This allows pupils with different ability levels to be working on the same activity in the one classroom. The activities increase in difficulty throughout the levels of the books. This allows for easy use within a multi-ability classroom.

Country	Subject/Year	Objectives	Book 1	Book 2	Book 3
England	English (Writing) KS 2	**Composition** • choose form and content to suit a particular purpose	•	•	•
		• broaden vocabulary and use it in inventive ways	•	•	•
		• use language and style appropriate to the reader	•	•	•
		• use and adapt the features of a form of writing, drawing on reading	•	•	•
		• use features of layout, presentation and organisation effectively	•	•	•
		Planning and drafting • plan – note and develop initial ideas	•	•	•
		• draft – develop ideas from the plan into structured written text	•	•	•
		• revise – change and improve the draft	•	•	•
		• proofread – check the draft for spelling and punctuation errors	•	•	•
		• present – present a neat, correct and clear final copy	•	•	•
		• discuss and evaluate their own and other's writing	•	•	•
		Punctuation • use punctuation marks correctly in writing	•	•	•
		Spelling • check spelling using dictionaries	•	•	•
		Breadth of study • write to imagine and explore feelings and ideas, focusing on creative uses of language and how to interest the reader	•	•	•
		• write narratives	•	•	•
Northern Ireland	English (Writing) KS 2	**Planning** • plan written work through discussion with teacher and other pupils, gathering and organising ideas, preparing an outline and making notes	•	•	•
		Purpose • write for a variety of purposes, including to narrate and to express their thoughts, feelings and imaginings	•	•	•
		Context • write in response to a variety of experiences and contexts, including first-hand experience and in response to their reading	•	•	•
		Range • write in different forms and develop control over the different conventions demanded by these forms, including stories (based on personal experience and books read), creative and imaginative writing and dialogues	•	•	•
		• develop increasing competence in the use of punctuation	•	•	•
		• discuss various features of layout in texts they are reading	•	•	•
		• use knowledge of the alphabet to locate the correct spelling of words	•	•	•
		Expected outcomes • make expressive use of language when describing imaginings	•	•	•
		• observe the different conventions and structures demanded by the various forms of writing	•	•	•
		• locate the correct spelling of words that they need to use in writing through dictionaries	•	•	•
		• set out and punctuate direct speech	•	•	•
Republic of Ireland	English (Writing) 3rd/4th Class	**Receptiveness** • experience a classroom environment that encourages writing	•	•	
		• observe the teacher modelling different writing genres	•	•	
		• use personal reading as a stimulus to writing	•	•	
		• write stories that explore a variety of genres	•	•	
		Competence and confidence • write regularly and gradually extend the period of time over which a writing effort is sustained	•	•	
		• engage with the writing of one piece over a period of time	•	•	
		• learn to use questions as a mechanism for expanding and developing a story	•	•	
		• give sequence to ideas and events in stories	•	•	
		• learn to revise and redraft writing	•	•	
		• learn to use a wider range of punctuation marks with greater accuracy as part of the revision and editing process	•	•	
		Developing cognitive abilities • write in a variety of genres; e.g. stories	•	•	
		Emotional and imaginative • create stories	•	•	
		• write extended stories in book form	•	•	
	English (Writing) 5th/6th Class	**Receptiveness** • experience a classroom environment that encourages writing		•	•
		• experience interesting and relevant writing challenges		•	•
		• receive and give constructive responses to writing		•	•

 **Curriculum links**

Country	Subject/Year	Objectives	Book 1	Book 2	Book 3
	English (Writing) 5th/6th Class	*Competence and confidence* • write regularly and for a sustained length of time • engage in the writing of one piece over a period of time • observe the teacher improving writing – drafting, revising, editing • write independently through a process of drafting, revising, editing and publishing • observe the conventions of grammar, punctuation and spelling in his/her writing • use dictionaries to develop spelling • help others with editing their writing *Developing cognitive abilities* • write in a wide variety of genres; e.g. narratives • refine ideas and expression through drafting and redrafting *Emotional and imaginative* • write longer stories		• • • • • • • • • •	• • • • • • • • • •
Scotland	English (Writing) Level B	*Imaginative writing* • draft writing using questions and writing model • discuss first drafts of writing • be aware of aspects of stories from reading; e.g. plot, character, dialogue and setting *Punctuation and structure* • use capital letters and full stops correctly *Spelling* • after drafting, mark possible spelling errors and check correct spellings using a dictionary *Knowledge about language* • plan, draft and redraft during the writing process	• • • • • •		
	English (Writing) Level C	*Imaginative writing* • develop awareness of the importance of character, setting the scene and action *Punctuation and structure* • use commas correctly • use co-operative writing and discussion to reinforce the role of audience and motivate redrafting *Spelling* • after drafting, mark possible spelling errors and check correct spellings using a dictionary *Knowledge about language* • consider purpose and audience when considering what they plan to write or have written	• • • •	• • • • •	
	English (Writing) Level D	*Punctuation and structure* • look at texts to help learn about direct speech *Spelling* • use self-correction techniques to deal with spelling errors • use dictionaries to check spelling at the end of drafting		• • •	• • •
	English (Writing) Level E	*Imaginative writing* • draw on knowledge of what they have heard and read to use in own imaginative writing • develop characters and settings • show awareness of openings and resolutions • write, discuss and redraft sections of stories before putting them together to build longer, more fully-shaped works *Punctuation and structure* • check punctuation and organisation as part of the redrafting process • discuss drafting in pairs or small groups *Spelling* • use self-correction techniques to deal with spelling errors • use dictionaries to check spelling at the end of drafting			• • • • • • • •
Wales	English (Writing) KS 2	*Range* • write in response to a wide range of stimuli, including stories • use the characteristics of different kinds of writing • write in forms which include imaginative writing *Skills* • plan, draft and improve their work • discuss and evaluate their own and others' writing • plan – note and develop initial ideas • draft – develop ideas from the plan into structured written text • revise – alter and improve the draft • proofread – check the draft for spelling and punctuation errors • present – prepare a neat, correct and clear final copy • develop ability to organise and structure work in a variety of ways, using experience of fiction texts; e.g. a story with a beginning, middle and end • use punctuation marks correctly in writing • check spellings using dictionaries • use features of layout and presentation	• • • • • • • • • • • • • •	• • • • • • • • • • • • • •	• • • • • • • • • • • • • •

DRAWING CHARACTERS

Objective

- Interprets texts with attention to main characters.

Teacher information

- Read the descriptive passage together.
- Underline the specific features that will need to be illustrated.
    - shirt [frilly and white]
    - kilt [red and black checked]
    - socks [long]
    - shoes [lace-up]
    - hat [black, shaped like a pancake with a pom-pom]
    - hair [red and curly]
    - eyes [blue and twinkly]
    - wide grin
- Which features leave room for the illustrator's own choice?
    - colour of socks, shoes and pom-pom
    - other facial features, such as freckles, size of nose, facial hair
    - length of hair
    - colour of skin

    Add other suggestions from the pupils.
- Encourage the pupils to complete the worksheet, focusing on colour and detail. Pupils use the detail provided in the passage and add some of their 'own choice' detail.

Additional activities

- Pupils compare their completed illustrations and discuss any differences. What implications are there for an illustrator who has been asked to illustrate a book? Discuss.
- Art lesson: Pupils produce a painting of Mr McGregor.
- Pupils write a new descriptive paragraph, which incorporates their added detail.

Assessment checklist

- Could the pupil underline specific features to be included in the illustration?
- Could the pupil suggest additional features for an illustration?
- Did the illustration match the specific features?
- Could the pupil create new descriptive sentences to match their picture?

DRAWING CHARACTERS

Think of your favourite story. What do you remember about the main characters? You may know what they look like, what kind of personality they have and whether they have any special characteristics. While you read the story, you have a clear picture of the characters in your mind.

1. Read the following description of a character called Mr McGregor. Underline the specific features of the character.

   'Mr McGregor wore a frilly white shirt tucked into his red and black checked kilt. He had long socks and lace-up shoes. On his head he wore a black hat shaped like a pancake with a pom-pom on top. Lots of red curly hair sprang out from underneath it. His bright blue eyes twinkled and a wide grin spread across his face.'

2. Draw a picture that matches the description.

DESCRIBING CHARACTERS

Objective

- Writes a short passage of text, using appropriate descriptive language to convey meaning.

Teacher information

- Write a basic descriptive character sentence on the board:

  e.g. 'Alison had brown hair and blue eyes.'

  Discuss adding other descriptive words (adjectives) to make the sentence as interesting and detailed as possible.

  1. Alison had short brown hair and pale blue eyes.

  2. Alison had short, curly brown hair and pale blue eyes.

  3. Alison had short, curly brown hair that stuck out at crazy angles and pale blue eyes with long black eyelashes.

- Compare the original version with the most detailed one. Which would be easier and more fun to illustrate?

- Continue the description to add more information until the pupils have created a detailed description that could be illustrated.

- Prepare piles of cards with descriptive features on them. Features could include:

  1. hair – blonde, brown, black, curly, straight, long, short, bald etc.

  2. eyes – different colours and sizes

  3. other facial features – bushy eyebrows, freckles, scar, skin colour

  Each pupil picks a card from each pile. These will be used as a starting point for the worksheet.

- Read through the worksheet as a class group. Encourage the pupils to complete their description first and then illustrate it, focusing on colour and detail. They must use their given characteristics, but then add detail of their own choice.

Additional activities

- In pairs, one pupil reads out his/her descriptive sentences while the partner draws the character. The pupils swap tasks and compare the two drawings at the end. How different is the author's illustration from the partner's?

- Each pupil picks new cards. Using a paint or drawing program on the computer, he/she creates a computer illustration of the character and uses text boxes to label particular features and write a description of the character.

Assessment checklist

- Did the pupil contribute ideas to the initial description on the board?

- Did the pupil incorporate the feature cards?

- Could the pupil add detail of his/her own choice?

- Did the pupil's illustration and description match?

- Did the pupil complete the computer activity?

DESCRIBING CHARACTERS

You are going to invent a character.

1. Decide on some of the features first, or choose your own.

    (a) Hair:

    blonde ☐   brown ☐   black ☐   red ☐   _____ ☐

    curly ☐   straight ☐   long ☐   short ☐   _____ ☐

    (b) Eyes:

    brown ☐   blue ☐   green ☐   hazel ☐   _____ ☐

    (c) Other features: _____

    _____

2. Write a detailed description of your character. Try to make it so detailed that someone reading your description would be able to imagine and draw the character.

    _____

    _____

    _____

    _____

    _____

    _____

    _____

    _____

    _____

    _____

    _____

    _____

    _____

    _____

3. Read your description again and draw a detailed picture of your character in colour.

CHARACTER WHEELS

Objectives

- Discusses a broad description of a person, paying attention to several distinguishing characteristics.

- Records ideas in a character wheel.

Teacher information

- Discuss the importance of other aspects of characterisation. Look at the character wheel and read the categories together. Draw a character wheel on the board and choose a main character from a well-known story. Fill in the character wheel for the chosen character as a class.

- Ask the pupils to think of their best friend and fill in as much detail as they can about them using the character wheel. (This can be done as an oral discussion exercise, on the board using a selected pupil, or by photocopying a second worksheet for the pupils to complete individually.)

- Remind the pupils about their created character from Characters 2. Encourage them to continue their character creation by filling in the character wheel about the same character, to create a more detailed description.

Additional activities

- Convert the information from the character wheel into a paragraph of information. Add this to the description from Characters 2.

- Pupils introduce their characters to the class.

- Pupils can repeat the exercise using the character wheel for their best friend.

Display idea

- Print out the computer illustration from Characters 2.

- Publish the new detailed description on a separate sheet of paper.

- Display the two pieces of work side by side.

Assessment checklist

- Did the pupil contribute to the class discussion?

- Was the pupil able to use the character wheel correctly?

- Did the pupil complete a character wheel for his/her character?

CHARACTER WHEELS

When you write a story, it is important to include interesting characters. You need to consider not just what they look like, but also how they behave, how they talk, their likes and dislikes etc. You can use character wheels like this one to keep all of this information together.

1. Choose a well-known character from a book you have read or a character from a story you are writing, and complete the character wheel about him or her.

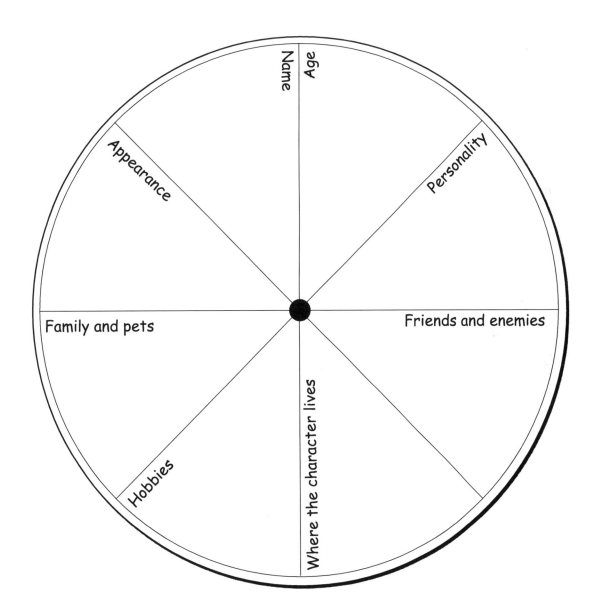

2. Think about your character. What are his or her likes and dislikes? (You can use your imagination.) Write them below.

Likes: _____   Dislikes: _____

_____   _____

_____   _____

CREATING CHARACTERS

Objective

- Plans a detailed description of a person to develop an overall image.

Teacher information

- Explain that this worksheet is a summary of the previous two. When completed, the pupils will have fully developed character summaries, incorporating appearance, personality and background information.

- Discuss the types of facts that could be included in each section of the worksheet.

  – appearance: age, height, hair, eye and skin colour, choice of clothes, facial features.

  – personality: friendly, shy, outgoing, cranky, sad, nervous? Does he or she have a particular trait?

  – other facts: where he/she lives, likes and dislikes, family members, friends etc.

- Discuss the use of point form to present information quickly and effectively.

  – Use the detailed example sentence about Alison.

    'Alison had short, curly brown hair that stuck out at crazy angles and pale blue eyes with long black eyelashes.'

  – Convert this sentence into point form.

    • short, curly, brown hair

    • hair sticks out at crazy angles

    • pale blue eyes

    • long black eyelashes

  – Repeat using sentences from the pupils' character wheels from the previous activity.

- Read the worksheet together as a class group. Pupils complete the worksheet individually.

Additional activities

- Discuss the idea that many authors use index card boxes to store their information about particular characters. Pupils may like to create their own index cards, adding more characters if they wish.

- Make and decorate a box in which to store the character cards.

Assessment checklist

- Does the pupil understand the difference between appearance and personality?

- Did the pupil fill in each section of the worksheet to create the characters?

- Did the pupil use point form?

CREATING CHARACTERS

You are going to invent two complex characters. You will consider their appearance and personality.

1. Include each character's likes, dislikes, family members, pets etc. in the 'Other Facts' box. Use this sheet to create two characters you could use as the main characters of a story.

Character Name:

Appearance:

Personality:

Other Facts:

Character Name:

Appearance:

Personality:

Other Facts:

EFFECTIVE DIALOGUE

Objective
- Understands that dialogue is composed of different elements.

Teacher information
- Discuss the idea that writing effective dialogue is important because it will bring characters to life and give readers extra information—such as the way the characters speak and how they react to certain events.

- Discuss the idea that dialogue can add humour or drama. It moves the story along and makes it easier to read.

- Important points to remember when writing dialogue:
  1. Make sure to choose words that match the age and personality of the characters.
  2. Dialogue needs to fit the mood and current events in the story.
  3. Good dialogue incorporates four things. All four things don't need to be included at once, but there should be a balance of them throughout the story.

     These are:
     - Spoken words – show what the character is saying
     - Speech tags – show which character is speaking
     - Actions – show what the character is doing
     - Thoughts – show what the character is thinking or feeling

Answers
'What do you think is going to happen?' **Sarah asked** Laura as they (got their bags that afternoon.)

'I don't know', **answered Laura**. 'Do you think Kate can do it?'

'Maybe.'

'I hope she does', **said Laura**. 'I'm sick of Josh thinking he's so tough.'

'Yeah', **agreed Sarah**. 'And his silly gang, following him around all the time. I'd like to see the look on their faces if Kate actually wins.'

Laura giggled. 'They'd probably start following her around instead!'

'Yuk!' (Kate appeared from behind them,) having overheard Laura's last comment. 'As if I'd want them following me!'

(The girls walked off together.) Laura and Sarah were (laughing and talking), but Kate walked quietly. What will happen if I don't win? she thought. Josh would never let me forget it.

Additional activities
- Pupils can repeat the exercise by choosing a random piece of dialogue from a favourite story. Alternatively, the class teacher can choose a particular piece of dialogue to analyse from a shared reading session.

- Suggestions for stories to use:
  – Any short story by Paul Jennings.
  – Harry Potter series by JK Rowling.
  – Deltora Quest series by Emily Rodda.

Assessment checklist
- Could the pupil identify the four elements of dialogue?

1.   Good dialogue is made up of four parts. Read each part carefully.

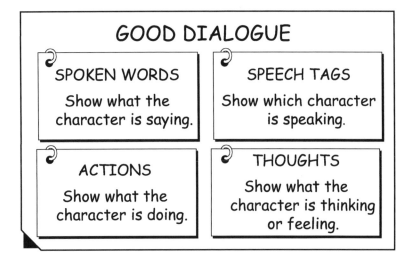

GOOD DIALOGUE

SPOKEN WORDS
Show what the character is saying.

SPEECH TAGS
Show which character is speaking.

ACTIONS
Show what the character is doing.

THOUGHTS
Show what the character is thinking or feeling.

2.   In the following piece of dialogue:

- underline the spoken words
- put brackets around the actions
- highlight the speech tags
- put a box around the thoughts

'What do you think is going to happen?' Sarah asked Laura as they got their bags that afternoon.

'I don't know', answered Laura. 'Do you think Kate can do it?'

'Maybe.'

'I hope she does', said Laura. 'I'm sick of Josh thinking he's so tough.'

'Yeah', agreed Sarah. 'And his silly gang, following him around all the time. I'd like to see the look on their faces if Kate actually wins.'

Laura giggled. 'They'd probably start following her around instead!'

'Yuk!' Kate appeared from behind them, having overheard Laura's last comment. 'As if I'd want them following me!'

The girls walked off together. Laura and Sarah were laughing and talking, but Kate walked quietly. What will happen if I don't win? she thought. Josh would never let me forget it.

DIALOGUE RULES

Objective

- Identifies the rules of writing dialogue.

Teacher information

- How to set out dialogue correctly

  1. Every time a new character speaks, you start a new paragraph; for example:

     'What did you think of the maths test?' asked Sari, as she and Tayla walked towards the canteen.

     'OK, I guess', answered Tayla.

  2. Everything the character says out loud is put inside the speech marks.

     - If there is no speech tag, the full stop is also inside the speech marks; for example:

       'That's exactly what I'm saying.'

     - If there is a speech tag, put a comma outside the speech marks and then add the speech tag; for example:

       'That's exactly what I'm saying', said Kate.

     - If there is a comma in what the character says, it goes inside the speech marks; for example:

       'The maths test was OK,' said Tayla, 'but I'm worried about the science test'.

  3. If the character speaks, then does something and then speaks again, you don't need to take a new line for the second lot of speech; for example:

     'That's exactly what I'm saying', said Kate. She picked up the book from the table. 'Come on, what are we waiting for?'

  4. If someone is talking and his/her words trail off, use three dots; for example:

     'It seems like only yesterday,' said Frank, sleepily. 'I remember ...'

  5. If someone is interrupted while talking, use a long dash; for example:

     'No, wait!' said Laura. 'Just listen for a—'

  6. Speech marks are not necessary if a character is thinking something without speaking aloud; for example:

     I can't believe it's so long until lunch, thought Ben, gloomily. I'm hungry right now!

Answers

1. (a) 3   (b) 1   (c) 4   (d) 5   (e) 2(a)   (f) 6   (g) 2(b)

Additional activity

- Pupils can repeat the exercise by choosing a random piece of dialogue from a favourite story. Alternatively, the class teacher can choose a particular piece of dialogue from a shared reading session to analyse.

Assessment checklist

- Could the pupil match the dialogue examples to the correct rule?

When writing dialogue, there are six important rules to follow.

These rules are:

'?'

1. Every time a new character speaks, you start a new paragraph.

2. Everything the character says out loud is put inside the speech marks.

    (a) If there is no speech tag, the full stop is also inside the speech marks; for example, 'The dog looks sick.'

    (b) If there is a speech tag, put a comma outside the speech marks and then add the speech tag; for example, 'The dog looks sick', said Missy.

    (c) If there is a comma in what the character says, it goes inside the speech marks; for example, 'The maths test was OK,' said Tayla, 'but I'm worried about the science test'.

3. If the character speaks, then does something and then speaks again, you don't need to take a new line for the second lot of speech.

4. If someone is talking and his/her words trail off, use three dots to finish the sentence.

5. If someone is interrupted while talking, use a long dash to finish the sentence.

6. Speech marks are not necessary if a character is thinking something without speaking aloud.

1. Read the following examples and match them to the correct dialogue rule. Write the number of the rule in the box.

    (a) 'That's exactly what I'm saying', said Kate. She picked up the book from the table. 'Come on, what are we waiting for?' ☐

    (b) 'What did you think of the maths test?' asked Sari, as she and Tayla walked towards the canteen.

    'OK, I guess,' answered Tayla. ☐

    (c) 'It seems like only yesterday', said Frank, sleepily. 'I remember ...' ☐

    (d) 'No, wait!' said Laura. 'Just listen for a—' ☐

    (e) 'That's exactly what I'm saying.' ☐

    (f) I can't believe it's so long until lunch, thought Ben, gloomily. I'm hungry right now! ☐

    (g) 'That's exactly what I'm saying', said Kate. ☐

DESIGNING DIALOGUE

Objective

• Uses direct speech.

Teacher information

• Review the rules of good dialogue, as well as the rules for setting out dialogue correctly.

• As a class, create a piece of dialogue as a group example.

Teacher provides the first sentence and accepts pupil suggestions. The following is an example:

'Hi, Sarah!' said Ben, as he opened the door.

'Hi, Ben!' said Sarah. She held out a present wrapped in brightly coloured paper. 'I hope you like it.'

'Thanks', said Ben. I wonder what it is, he thought, tearing the paper. 'Oh wow!' he said, unwrapping a new CD. 'It's great!'

• Pupils are then encouraged to complete the worksheet individually, using the characters they created.

Additional activities

• Pupils share their completed pieces of dialogue with each other.

• Repeat analysis of dialogue from page 10, using the pupil's dialogue as the example.

Assessment checklist

• Could the pupil recall the rules of good dialogue?

• Did the pupil create a piece of dialogue incorporating these rules?

• Was the dialogue set out correctly?

DESIGNING DIALOGUE

You are going to write a short piece of dialogue between two characters.

1. Complete the information below to help you.

   • Name of character 1:   • Name of character 2:

   _____   _____

   • Characters are discussing: _____

   _____

   • Characters are:

   two friends ☐   brother and sister ☐   father and child ☐

   two neighbours ☐   teacher and pupil ☐   _____ ☐

2. Write your dialogue below. Remember the four parts of good dialogue and set your writing out correctly.

HANDY HINTS

○ Have you used speech tags?

○ What are the characters doing?

○ Are there actions involved?

○ What are the characters thinking?

3. Read your dialogue again. How could you improve it?

DEVELOPING DIALOGUE

Objective

- Writes a passage of increased complexity, using imaginative and correctly constructed dialogue.

Teacher information

- Review the piece of dialogue created as a group example.

- Brainstorm how this scene could be continued, by adding new characters and dialogue.

  Example of continued scene between Ben and Sarah (from page 14).

  Ben's mum walked out of the kitchen. 'Hi, Sarah!' she said. 'Come into the lounge room. Would you like a drink?'

  'Yes, please, Mrs Wilson', said Sarah, as she followed Ben down the hallway.

  Ben's dad was in the lounge room, hanging balloons off the ceiling fan.

  'Hi, Mr Wilson!' said Sarah. 'Do you need some help?'

  Just then, the doorbell rang.

  'Come on, Sarah', said Ben. 'Let's see who that is.'

  I wonder how many people are coming to the party, thought Sarah.

- Pupils are encouraged to look at their own scene from the previous worksheet and think about how they could continue the scene.

- Pupils complete the worksheet individually.

Additional activities

- Pupils share their completed pieces of dialogue with each other.

- Link with drama: Pupils act out their scene, using a narrator to read the actions and the speech tags.

Assessment checklist

- Did the pupil participate in the brainstorming session?

- Did the pupil continue his/her dialogue?

- Was the dialogue set out correctly?

DEVELOPING DIALOGUE

Using the dialogue you created in Dialogue 3, page 15 you are going to introduce two more characters and continue the conversation with the bigger group.

1. Complete the information below to help you.

    •   Name of character 3:   •   Name of character 4:

    _____   _____

2. (a) Character 3 is a: friend ☐ teacher ☐ neighbour ☐

        doctor ☐ parent ☐ _____ ☐

    (b) Character 4 is a: friend ☐ teacher ☐ neighbour ☐

        doctor ☐ parent ☐ _____ ☐

3. Write your dialogue below. Remember the four parts of good dialogue and set your writing out correctly.

_____

_____

_____

_____

_____

_____

_____

_____

_____

_____

_____

HANDY HINTS
- What will happen next?
- What are the characters thinking?
- Who will join the characters next?
- Don't forget the actions!

4. Read your dialogue again. How could you improve it?

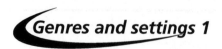

STORY GENRES

Objective

*   Understands conventions of particular text types.

Teacher information

*   Useful stories by genre

Family/School stories:	Hannah series by Libby Gleeson *Cabbage patch war* by Paul Jennings *Tales of a fourth grade nothing* by Judy Blume Assorted titles by Jacqueline Wilson
Animal stories:	Selby series by Duncan Ball *Fantastic Mr Fox* by Roald Dahl *Wind in the willows* by Kenneth Graeme
Mystery stories:	Emily Eyefinger series by Duncan Ball *Finders keepers* by Emily Rodda Famous Five and Secret Seven series by Enid Blyton
Action/Adventure:	Tashi series by Anna Fienberg *Horrendo's curse* by Anna Fienberg
History stories:	*The silver sword* by Ian Serraillier *Arthur: The seeing stone* by Kevin Crossley-Holland
Science fiction and fantasy:	Harry Potter series by JK Rowling *The Hobbit* by JRR Tolkien

*   Brainstorm titles of favourite class stories.

*   Read definitions of story genres as a class group. Match the story titles with their appropriate genre.

*   Pupils complete the worksheet individually.

Additional activities

*   Pupils share their answers with each other. Discuss the concept that stories can often overlap between genres.

*   Link with information technology: Construct a table to show the different possible genres for each story; for example:

Story title	Main genre	Other genre
The Hobbit	Fantasy	Action/Adventure

Assessment checklist

*   Did the pupil participate in the class discussion regarding different genres?

*   Could the pupil identify an appropriate genre for the list of stories given?

*   Could the pupil identify an appropriate genre for stories of their own choice?

There are many different types of stories. These story types are called genres.

1. Read the definitions of the following story genres. Think of at least one example of each genre from the stories/books you have read. Write your example in the box.

    (a) **Science fiction/Fantasy:** [ ]

    In these stories, the characters exist in a different world from the one we live in. The places and names may sound different from ours.

    (b) **Historical fiction:** [ ]

    These stories are based around a specific time in history. The author researches that time so the story sounds authentic.

    (c) **Action/Adventure:** [ ]

    These stories are fast paced with twists and turns, and possible danger for the main character. The story usually has lots of excitement to make the reader want to turn the pages quickly.

    (d) **Mystery:** [ ]

    The characters in these stories usually have a puzzle to solve. As the characters try to solve the mysterious puzzle, they make mistakes and face danger. The ending is usually very exciting.

    (e) **Animal stories:** [ ]

    In these stories, the animals are the important characters. Sometimes the animals will help human characters or they might think and talk—behaving just like humans.

    (f) **Family and school stories:** [ ]

    These stories develop in a family or school setting. The problems to be solved are usually ones in everyday life so these stories are often the easiest to write.

2. (a) Which story genre do you like reading the most?

    _____

    (b) When you write a creative story, which genre do you usually choose?

    _____

    (c) Why do you choose this genre?

    _____

    _____

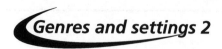
STORY SETTINGS

Objective

- Understands that writers need to bring readers into the world of text, by setting the scene clearly.

Teacher information

- Explain to the class that the setting is where the story takes place; for example, in a forest, a school or on the moon.

- Discuss the concept that effective description makes the reader feel as if he/ she is in the place described. The most effective way to do this is to use the five senses—sight, sound, taste, touch and smell.

- Ask the pupils to list the five senses. Take them on a 'senses walk' around the school. Instruct them to take notice of what they can see, hear, smell, touch or taste. On returning, brainstorm answers for each sense. (Sight and sound will probably be the most popular. Encourage creative suggestions for the others.) Ask the pupils to create sentences that describe the school building in terms of the senses. Use the following focus questions:

  1. What did you see?

  2. What did you hear?

  3. What did you smell?

  4. What did you feel?

  (Not all senses need to be used, but the more that are used, the better.)

- Read through the worksheet as a class group. After a brief discussion, pupils complete the worksheet.

Answers

1. sight, smell, taste, touch, sound

Possible answers

3. (a) train tunnel, sunlight

   (b) wind, muffled birdcalls, running water

   (c) pupils will need to use their imagination

   (d) fresh, cold water

   (e) smooth walls, jacket, water in a running stream

4. Teacher check

Additional activity

- Pupils compare their answers. In small groups, they can then choose a passage from a story of their own choice and repeat the analysis. The groups report back to the class.

Assessment checklist

- Could the pupil list the five senses?

- Did the pupil contribute to the class creation of a senses description?

- Could the pupil identify the senses within a given descriptive passage?

Once you have chosen the type of story you are going to write, you need to choose the setting. The setting is where the action takes place. Will your characters travel to different places? These will need to be described also.

When you describe the setting of your story, you can use the senses to make it more interesting.

1. List the five senses below.

2. Read the following passage:

> Steven looked around in surprise. Where was he? He was standing in what looked like a train tunnel. There were smooth walls on either side of him, but there were no train tracks beneath his feet. The wind whistled through the tunnel and he pulled his jacket closer around him for warmth. He became aware of the sound of muffled birdcalls in the distance and he could see sunlight through the cracks in the walls. As his ears became accustomed to the noises around him, he heard the sound of running water. He walked through the tunnel, towards the sound. After a few moments, he emerged into a forest clearing with a running stream. He cupped his hands and drank the fresh, cold water.

3. Answer the following questions about the passage you have just read. You will need to use your imagination for one answer.

    (a) What can the character see?

    _____

    _____

    _____

    (b) What can the character hear?

    _____

    _____

    _____

    (c) What can the character smell?

    _____

    _____

    (d) What can the character taste?

    _____

    _____

    (e) What can the character touch?

    _____

    _____

    _____

4. On the back of this sheet, draw the setting described in the paragraph. Use colour to make it 'come to life'.

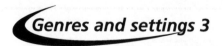
USING THE SENSES

Objective

• Writes a detailed description of a scene or place, choosing details to convey a specific impression of it to someone else.

Teacher information

• Review the different story genres from the worksheet on page 19. What sorts of settings would match the particular genres?

• Brainstorm a list of settings for each story genre on the board.

Example settings:

Science fiction/fantasy – space, the future, mountainous landscape, a different planet etc.

Family/School – modern day house, school etc.

Animal – forest, jungle, farm etc.

Mystery – old building, deserted town, place with hidden trapdoors or secret pathways etc.

History – 50 years or earlier in any given country. Remember to consider: transport, clothing, houses, ways of communication etc.

Action/Adventure: airport, on board a train, bus, car – or any of the above genre settings.

Fairytale – castle, swamp, forest etc.

Myths and legends – mythical past, ancient times etc.

• As a class group, pick one genre to work with. Construct a description of the setting for the chosen genre, using as many of the senses as possible. Use adjectives to bring the text to life. Can the pupils imagine the setting in their minds?

• Each pupil chooses a genre and a possible setting to complete the worksheet.

Additional activities

• Pupils share their descriptions.

• Discuss the following questions, based on the shared work:

1. How many pupils picked the same genre?

2. How were their descriptions similar or different?

3. Which were the most effective? Why?

Assessment checklist

• Could the pupil suggest appropriate settings for each genre?

• Could the pupil write a description that incorporated adjectives and the five senses?

USING THE SENSES

1. Choose a genre.

☐ Science fiction and fantasy

☐ Action/Adventure

☐ Animal stories

☐ Fairytale

☐ Historical fiction

☐ Mystery

☐ Family and school stories

☐ Myths and legends

2. Consider some possible settings for a story in the genre you have chosen. List them. Circle the one that appeals to you the most.

3. Write a paragraph that describes the setting you chose above. Include adjectives and some or all of the senses in your description. Draw your setting in the box.

HANDY HINTS

o What can you see or hear?

o What can you touch?

o What can you smell?

o What can you taste?

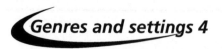
CREATING A SCENE

Objectives

- Writes a complex description of a scene or place, choosing details to convey a specific impression of it to someone else.
- Includes dialogue in the description.

Teacher information

- Review the list of genres and settings from page 22.
- Encourage pupils to pick a different genre.
- Review character creation and the correct use of dialogue.
- Read through the worksheet together. Explain the steps: describing a setting using the senses, introducing two characters and writing a short piece of dialogue.

  Suggest that one character is describing the scene, then meets the second character and they have a conversation. An opening sentence could be: *'Tom walked up the old stone pathway and pushed open the creaky door ...'* [description continues]

Additional activities

- Pupils share their work.
- Group pupils according to their chosen genre. Pupils read their individual description. How similar or different are the settings?

Assessment checklist

- Could the pupil recall elements of characterisation and dialogue?
- Did the pupil's description use the five senses?
- Could the pupil introduce two characters?
- Was the dialogue presented correctly?

CREATING A SCENE

1. Choose a story genre. _____

2. Consider some possible settings for a story in the genre you have chosen. List them in the box.

   Circle the one that appeals to you most.

3. Which two characters will be in your chosen setting? (Make sure they match the genre of your story.)

   Character 1:   **Character 2:**

   _____   _____

4. Write a paragraph that describes the setting of your story and includes dialogue between the two characters.

   For example, an opening sentence could be:

   'Tom walked up the old stone pathway and pushed open the creaky door ...' (Tom then meets someone on the other side of the door.)

HANDY HINTS

o What will your characters say to each other?

o Remember to set out your dialogue correctly.

o Do the characters discuss the setting?

o Don't forget to use the senses and adjectives to describe the setting.

STORY PLANS

Objective

- Understands and experiments with narrative structure by writing story beginnings.

Teacher information

- Introduce the overall structure of a story. Remind the pupils that it is important to plan out what is going to happen. There needs to be a beginning that captures the reader's attention; a middle that keeps the action going; and an effective, satisfying ending. The combination of all three forms the story's plot.

The Beginning:	The author needs to 'hook' his/her readers right from the start, so that they will want to keep reading. The easiest way to do this is to start with something already happening; for example, a conversation, a problem, something unexpected.
The Middle:	Keep the action going! Get the characters solving problems, but make sure that there is always something else they need to do. Build up to the biggest event or problem and leave a few clues along the way.
The Ending:	The characters should work out how to solve the problem themselves. Make sure the ending fits in with the rest of the story.

- Read the worksheet activity as a group. Discuss the idea that without an effective beginning, the rest of the story may not be read!

- Encourage the pupils to follow the steps to complete the worksheet.

Additional activities

- Each pupil reads out one of his/her two sentence hooks. Class vote: Which story sounds the most interesting? (The voting can be by secret ballot if necessary.)

- Put all the sentence hooks into a hat and have each pupil draw one out. Write the next paragraph of the story, following on from the hook.

Assessment checklist

- Did the pupil demonstrate an understanding of story structure?
- Did the pupil use the steps to create an effective two-sentence hook?

When writing a story, the aim is to grab the reader's attention right from the start. Some authors use a 'two-sentence hook' to capture their reader's attention—making them want to read more.

There are two steps involved in creating a 'hook'.

> • *Start with a sentence that is immediately interesting.*
>
> • *Follow it with a second sentence that keeps the reader guessing.*

1. Read the following story beginnings.

(a) Kate Thompson held her breath and waited. In a few minutes, it would all be over.

(b) The door slammed shut! Darkness filled the room.

(c) 'Not in a thousand years!' Alley tore the letter into little pieces and threw them into the air above Noah's head.

(d) Austin carefully opened the crumpled and decaying paper. Please let this be a map! he thought.

2. Which story beginning do you think is the most interesting?

   Explain why.

   (a) ☐
   (b) ☐
   (c) ☐
   (d) ☐

3. Write your own 'two-sentence hooks'. Make them as interesting as you can.

   • _____

   _____

   • _____

   _____

   • _____

   _____

MAKING AN IDEAS PACK

Objective

- Creates an 'ideas' set of cards to use when writing creative stories.

Teacher information

- Read through the instructions with the class. On the board, brainstorm a list of ideas for each category.

- Pupils can use some of the brainstormed ideas from the board for each category or create their own.

- Instruct pupils:

  - 'Who' set of cards: Write a different character on each card; for example, a teacher, old lady, alien, mad scientist, pirate.

  - 'Where' set of cards: Write a different place on each card; for example, shops, beach, jungle, city, space.

  - 'What' set of cards: Write a different object on each card; for example, pen, book, spoon, map, wallet.

  - 'Drama' set of cards: Write a dramatic or exciting event on each card; for example, being followed, winning a contest, losing something valuable.

- Pupils may also wish to include a small picture on each card.

- Encourage the pupils to assemble their ideas packs, using as many of their own ideas as possible.

- After completion, cut out each card and shuffle each separate pile. Lay them out in order; for example, 'Old lady', 'shop', 'book', 'being followed'.

- It is important that the pupil retains his/her cards for further activities.

- Look at the first three cards selected. Review the steps for writing a two-sentence hook from page 27. Create a two-sentence hook as a class group; for example:

  'Slowly, Grandma Williams opened the door of the secondhand book shop. It was time to say goodbye.'

- With their completed ideas packs, pupils select their own cards and write an interesting two-sentence hook to match the cards, on a separate sheet of paper.

  Teachers may wish to collect all of the pupils' cards and laminate them. The cards could be placed in separate 'who', 'what', 'where' and 'drama' boxes that are available to the pupils during creative writing.

Additional activities

- Pupils share their 'hooks' with each other.

- Pupils swap the cards with a friend and write a two-sentence hook for their friend's cards.

Assessment checklist

- Did the pupil contribute to the brainstorming list?

- Did the pupil create an ideas pack?

- Could the pupil use his/her ideas pack to create a two-sentence hook?

MAKING AN IDEAS PACK

Sometimes when you have to write a story, your mind goes blank.
Using an 'ideas' set of cards can help you.

1. Write a single idea on each card.

2. Cut out each set and shuffle them.

3. Select one card from each set and start writing!

    (You may like to add a picture if there is room.)

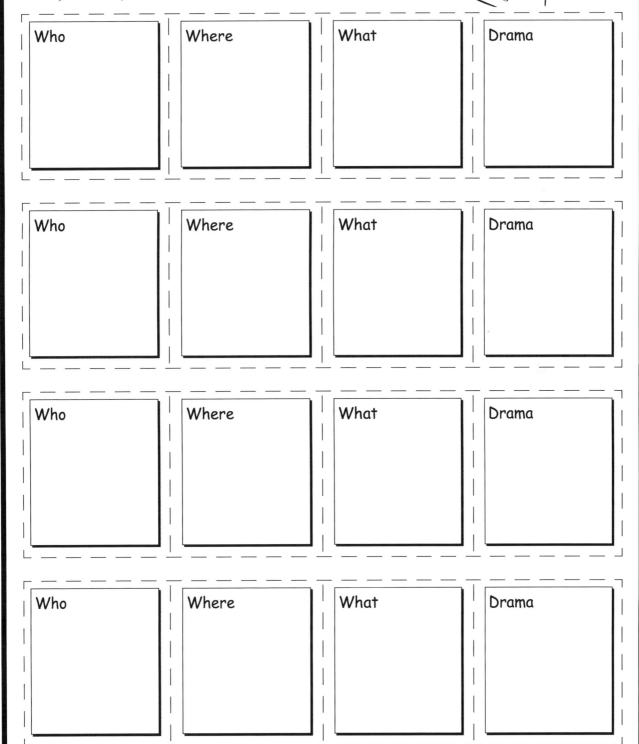

Who	Where	What	Drama
Who	Where	What	Drama
Who	Where	What	Drama
Who	Where	What	Drama

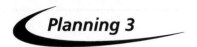
THE STORY PATH

Objective
- Draws on planning strategies that assist in effectively creating a story.

Teacher information
- Revise the structure of a story from page 26.
- As a class group, review the chosen cards from the ideas pack and create a story structure. A possible story could be:

  Beginning: *An old lady enters a secondhand shop and donates a book.*

  Middle: *After leaving the shop, she thinks she is being followed. She manages to lose the person following her. When she gets to her house, a stranger is waiting for her.*

  Ending: *The stranger turns out to be a shop assistant. An old letter had been found in the back of the book she had donated and the assistant is returning it.*

- Read through the steps on the story path.
- As a group, create a story path for this story. What needs to go in each step?

Possible answers
1. A description of the old lady; includes adjectives.
2. To donate her book.
3. Thinks she is being followed; manages to lose the person following her.
4. A stranger is waiting outside the house.
5. The stranger is from the shop and only wants to return the letter.

- Discuss the idea that each step needs more detail and that each pupil may have different descriptions and ideas.
- Pupils complete the activity, making any changes they like to the group story path.

Additional activities
- Pupils share their ideas.
- Using large sheets of paper, paint a story path for display in the classroom.
- Display individual worksheets of completed story paths.
- Pupils write the story using the information on the worksheet.

Assessment checklist
- Could the pupil recall the structure of a story?
- Could the pupil suggest answers for each step?
- Did the pupil complete the story path, adding details when necessary?

These 'ideas' cards have been chosen.

Who:

Where:

What:

Drama:

This is the story beginning.

An old lady enters a secondhand shop and donates a book.

In your group, make a path for your story to follow.
Discuss each part then write your ideas on the stones.

HANDY HINTS
o Is there something special about the shop?
o What is so special about the book?
o Why would someone be following her?
o Who is following the old lady?

1. Describe your character.

2. What does your character want to do?

3. What problems will your character face?

5. How is the problem solved?

4. What is the main drama in the story?

PATH OF IDEAS

Objective

- Selects a planning strategy to create a structured narrative.

Teacher information

- Explain to the pupils that this is an individual activity, which follows the previous whole-class activity on page 31. The steps will be the same, except that they will be completed by each pupil individually, rather than the whole class.

- Each pupil selects the required cards from his/her ideas pack.

- Each pupil creates a story path for the selected cards, adding detail to the steps as necessary.

- Instruct the pupils to create a story structure first, using the 'who', 'what' and 'where' cards for the story beginning and the 'drama' card for the middle.

- Pupils will need to create their own satisfying ending where the problems are solved.

Additional activities

- Pupils share their completed work.
- Display completed story paths.

Display idea

- Paint a large footpath with individual stepping stones on paper on the back wall of the classroom. Each pupil copies his/her story structure onto a single stone.

Assessment checklist

- Did the pupil use the ideas pack correctly?
- Did the pupil create a story path, adding detail when necessary?

1. Choose four 'ideas' cards. Record the cards you have chosen.

Who: [ ]   What: [ ]

Where: [ ]   Drama: [ ]

2. Write a story beginning. Your 'two-sentence hook' should capture the reader's attention and make him or her want to read more.

[ ]

3. Complete the story path.

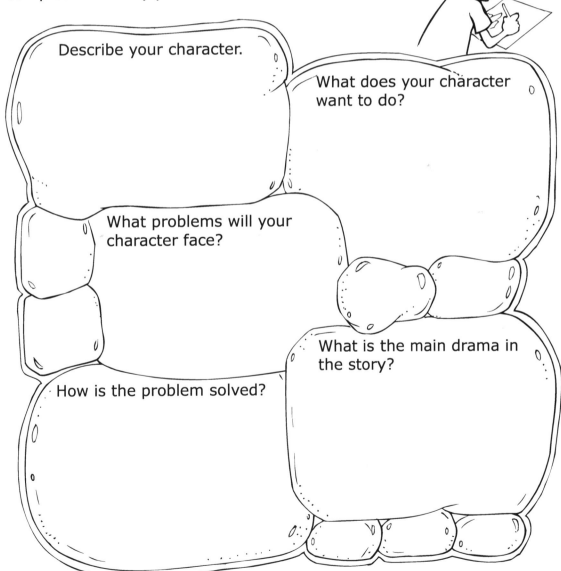

Describe your character.

What does your character want to do?

What problems will your character face?

What is the main drama in the story?

How is the problem solved?

BEGINNING A STORY

Objective

- Drafts the beginning of a narrative with attention to characterisation and order of events.

Teacher information

- Review the concepts of characterisation, dialogue and structure of a story.

- Explain to the pupils that they are going to use all the elements they have learnt about so far, to create a complete story.

- Pupils can use the story from their story path, since it is already planned, as opposed to starting a new story.

- Encourage the pupils to use this page for free writing. They will be able to edit and revise later, but for now should concentrate on getting the story written.

- Pupils focus on the beginning of the story and complete the worksheet. (Extra copies of the worksheet may be needed for very keen writers!)

- Pupils share their story beginning with a partner and discuss how it could be improved.

Additional activities

- Pupils share their work with the group.

- Pupils could provide some illustrations for the story so far, to be included for presentation and/or display.

Assessment checklist

- Could the pupil recall the concepts of characterisation, dialogue and story structure?

- Did the pupil follow the story plan to begin the story?

- Did the story begin with a two-sentence hook?

- Were characters and settings introduced?

- Did the pupil share his/her work with a partner and ask for positive criticism?

It is now time to put everything you have learnt together and write a short story of your own.

1. Write the beginning of your story.

   Remember to:

   - begin your story with a two-sentence hook

   - introduce your characters and the setting. Make your characters as detailed as possible, including their appearance and personality

   - follow the dialogue rules

HANDY HINTS

- o Look at your story path. Use Steps 1 and 2.

- o Your two-sentence hook should immediately capture the reader's attention.

- o Introduce the characters from your story.

- o Describe the setting using adjectives and the senses.

- o Include the thoughts and actions of the characters.

2. Ask a friend to read your story beginning. Discuss how you could improve it. Make notes.

CONTINUING A STORY

Objective

- Drafts the middle of an imaginative story with a distinguishable storyline.

Teacher information

- Explain to the class that they will now draft the middle of their story.

- Ask the pupils to reread the beginning of their story. The purpose of rereading at this stage is to get a clear idea of where the story is. Pupils should not be concerned with editing at this point.

- Review the structure of a story. Remind the pupils that in this worksheet they will continue the story, introducing some small problems along the way. This section should end with the introduction of the biggest problem in the story; i.e. the most dramatic part.

- Pupils share their story middle with a partner and discuss how it could be improved.

Additional activities

- Pupils share their work with the group.

- Pupils could provide some illustrations for the middle of the story, to be included for presentation and/or display.

Assessment checklist

- Could the pupil recall the structure of a story?

- Did this section of the story flow on from the beginning section?

- Did the pupil continue to follow the story path?

- Does this section end at the most dramatic point?

- Did the pupil share his/her work with a partner and ask for positive criticism?

CONTINUING A STORY

1. Read the beginning of your story.

2. You are now going to continue the story by writing the middle. In the middle, the characters are faced with small problems. They may solve some of them. The middle should end with the biggest problem or drama.

HANDY HINTS

o Look at step 3 of your story path.

o Introduce some small problems for your characters.

o What are the characters doing and thinking?

o Include dialogue between your characters.

o End with the most dramatic part of your story.

3. Ask a friend to read the middle of your story. Discuss how you could improve it. Make notes.

ENDING A STORY

Objective

- Drafts the end of an imaginative story with a distinguishable storyline in which some events are clearly related to the resolution of a problem.

Teacher information

- Explain to the class that they will now complete their story.
- Ask pupils to reread the first two sections of their story for content rather than correction.
- Discuss the ending of the story. Remind the pupils that they now have to tie up the loose ends, by having the problems resolved.
- Discuss the fact that not all endings are happy. It is fine to have a sad ending, as long as everything has been resolved and makes sense to the reader.
- Pupils complete their individual story.

Additional activities

- Pupils share their work with the group.
- Pupils could provide some illustrations for the final section of the story, to be included for presentation and/or display.
- Pupils share their story beginning with a partner and discuss how it could be improved.

Assessment checklist

- Did the pupil reread his/her story for content?
- Was the pupil able to contribute to the discussion about the ending of a story?
- Did the pupil's ending resolve the biggest problem in the story in an effective way?
- Did the pupil share his/her work with a partner and ask for positive criticism?

ENDING A STORY

1. You will now write the ending of your story. Your characters need to work out how to solve their problems.

HANDY HINTS

o Look at Step 5 of your story path.

o How will the main problem be solved?

o Remember the dialogue rules.

o Is there a hero in your story?

o Have all of the 'loose ends' been tied up?

---

2. Ask a friend to read your story ending. Discuss how you could improve it. Make notes below.

COVER IT

Objective

- Consider the presentation of book covers with regard to their impact on the reader.

Teacher information

- Display a number of front covers of various novels, short stories and picture books. Depending on the time of the year, this lesson could link with 'Book Week' activities.

- What elements make the cover effective?

    - Discuss the use of colour and design.

    - What picture has been used? Does it suggest something about the story?

    - What style of writing is used? Which part is in the biggest print?

    - Does the cover seem to match the title?

- What things are always included on a front cover?

    Title of story

    Name of author

    Name of illustrator

    Name of publisher

- Pupils complete the worksheet individually.

Additional activities

- Linking with art and design: pupils use a medium of their own choice to create their front cover; e.g. paint, photography, computer graphics.

- Display the completed front covers in the classroom.

Assessment checklist

- Did the pupil participate in the discussion of effective book covers?

- Could the pupil identify the common elements of a book cover?

- Did the pupil design an effective book cover for his/her own story?

1. Look at the front cover of your favourite book. What things make it an effective front cover?

_____

_____

_____

_____

2. Invent a title for your imaginary story.

Write it below.

_____

_____

_____

3. Design the front cover. Don't forget to include a colourful picture and your name as the author and illustrator.

PRACTISING REVISING

Objective

- Experiments with strategies for proofreading text and his/her own writing.

Teacher information

- Explain to the class that they will be reading text that needs to be revised. If available, copy the text onto an overhead transparency so that Questions 1 and 2 can be completed as a whole class.

- Read the text together once. Read Question 2 and explain that the aim is to find the mistakes in the text.

- As you read the text again, ask pupils to tell you when they see an error. Mark the errors and corrections on the board. The pupils then copy these corrections onto their own worksheet. Note: More able pupils could complete the worksheet independently.

- Let the class know that they have been 'editing' or 'revising' the story. Revising is one of the most important stages of writing. No author writes a perfect story on the first draft.

- Review the rules of setting out dialogue before the pupils complete Question 3.

Making revision beads

Materials per pupil:
- five hollow beads
- wool or string

Note: Have a needle available for threading the beads, for pupils who may find this task difficult.

- Pupils make their revision beads. These beads can be used whenever a piece of writing needs improving. Each time an error is found or a phrase/sentence is improved, the pupils will move a bead across.

- Pupils keep their revision beads with them during literacy lessons.

The beads will encourage the pupils to check their writing before they announce that they are finished.

Answers

'It was **your** fault!' yelled Patrick.

'No, it wasn't! It was **yours**!' Anne yelled back.

Patrick checked under the settee. 'Stop <u>whining</u> and help me look,' he said. 'Maybe Tick has <u>crept</u> back inside again.'

'You weren't supposed to let her go outside,' said **A**nne.

'I didn't!'

'Yes you did, you <u>opened</u> the door.'

Additional activities

- Pupils can make different revision tools, using different materials.

- Pupils compare their corrected text in Question 3 with a partner. How similar/different are they?

Assessment checklist

- Did the pupil follow the instructions to create a story revision tool?

- Could the pupil find the spelling mistakes in the text?

- Could the pupil find the missing full stops and commas in the text?

- Could the pupil circle the two letters that should be capital letters in the text?

- Could the pupil use a dictionary to find the correct spelling of the misspelt words?

- Could the pupil rewrite the text with each new character speaking on a new line?

- For more activities that develop and improve revision skills, see 'Proofreading and Editing Skills' by Prim-Ed Publishing.

1. Read the text.

> 'It was **your** fault!' yelled Patrick.
>
> 'No, it wasn't! It was **yours**!' Anne yelled back.
>
> patrick checked under the settee 'Stop whinning and help
>
> me look' he said. 'Maybe Tick has crepped back inside again'
>
> 'You weren't supposed to let her go outside' said anne.
>
> 'I didn't!'
>
> 'Yes you did, you openned the door.'

2. The text needs to be revised. In the text:

   - highlight the two letters that should be capital letters

   - underline the three spelling mistakes and write the correct spelling above the words

   - write in two missing full stops

   - add two missing commas

3. One of the rules of setting out dialogue is:

   Every time a new character speaks, you start a new paragraph.

   Rewrite the text using this rule. Edit your story by adding your corrections.

   > To make revising writing more fun, some authors move a coin, marble or stone from a pile across their desk for every correction. Others use revision beads. Try making your own set of beads.

_____

_____

_____

_____

_____

_____

_____

_____

_____

_____

_____

REVISING THE BEGINNING

Objectives

- Experiments with strategies for proofreading his/her own writing.
- Presents a revised version of a story beginning.

Teacher information

- Pupils need to have completed activity: 'Drafting – 1: Beginning a story' (page 35) prior to this activity.

- Once the pupils have completed their stories, introduce the editing stage. Explain to the class that they will now revise their story. Revising is one of the most important stages of writing. No author writes a perfect story on the first draft.

- Pupils will need a copy of the beginning of their story with them ('Beginning a story' – page 35). Explain to the class that they will only be revising the beginning part of their story in this lesson. This may only be one or two paragraphs. A whole lesson has been allocated for this so pupils will have time not only to find mistakes, but to improve their story if required.

- Discuss the concept that it is a good idea to take a break in between finishing the story and starting to revise it. It is easier to find mistakes and text that needs improving after leaving the writing for a while. (Teachers may wish to start the revision stage on a Monday.)

- Explain to the class what is required at each step of the worksheet. Encourage pupils to read aloud to see if their writing sounds correct. Pupils may work in pairs and ask their partner if they think their writing sounds correct and if their story is interesting. Remind pupils to make the corrections onto their draft worksheet.

- Remind pupils that they have completed activities that should help them to create an effective story beginning. Pupils can look at previous activities, such as:

    - 'Describing characters' (Page 5)
    - 'Effective dialogue'   (Page 11)
    - 'Dialogue rules'   (Page 13)
    - 'Creating a scene'   (Page 25)
    - 'Story plan'   (Page 27)

- Pupils proofread and edit the beginning of their story. They write the revised version onto the worksheet—using the back of the sheet if necessary.

Additional activities

- Pupils use the checklist on the worksheet to edit other pieces of their writing.
- Pupils keep a dictionary of misspelt words that they can include in their weekly spelling lists.

Assessment checklist

- Did the pupil mark corrections onto his/her own first draft?
- Did the pupil use a dictionary to correct spelling errors?
- Did the pupil read his/her work aloud—either to himself/herself or to a partner?
- Did the pupil present/publish the edited version onto the worksheet?

REVISING THE BEGINNING

Revising is a very important part of writing. No-one can write a perfect story on the first draft! You will now look for mistakes and ways to improve your story.

1. Reread the beginning of your story.

2. Edit your story.

   (a) Circle words that you think are misspelt. Use a dictionary to check them and write the correct spelling.

   (b) Add in any missing punctuation. Look for missing full stops, capital letters, commas and apostrophes.

   (c) Check that you have followed the rules of dialogue.

   – When a new character speaks, start a new paragraph. ☐

   – If there is a speech tag, the comma goes outside the speech marks, unless it is part of the speech. ☐

   – Include what the characters are doing and thinking. ☐

   Add your edits to your dialogue.

3. Does your story beginning:

   • 'hook' the reader in the first two sentences? Yes No

   • describe the setting? Yes No

   • introduce the characters? Yes No

   If you answered 'no', redraft parts of your beginning.

4. Present the corrected beginning of your story below.

   _____
   _____
   _____
   _____
   _____
   _____
   _____
   _____
   _____
   _____
   _____

REVISING THE MIDDLE

Objectives

- Experiments with strategies for proofreading his/her own writing.
- Presents a revised version of the middle of his/her own story.

Teacher information

- Pupils need to have completed activity:

  'Drafting – 2: Continuing a story' (page 37) prior to this activity.

- Explain to the class that they will now revise the middle of their story. Revising is one of the most important stages of writing. No author writes a perfect story on the first draft.

- Pupils will need a copy of the middle of their story with them ('Continuing a story' – page 37). Explain to the class that they will only be revising the middle part of their story in this lesson. This may only be one or two paragraphs. A whole lesson has been allocated for this so pupils will have time to not only find mistakes, but to improve their story if required.

- Explain to the class what is required at each step of the worksheet. Encourage pupils to read aloud to see if their writing sounds correct. Pupils may work in pairs and ask their partner if they think their writing sounds correct and if their story is interesting. Remind pupils to make the corrections onto their draft worksheet.

- Remind pupils that they have completed activities that should help them to create an effective story middle. Pupils can look at previous activities, such as:
  - 'Effective dialogue' (Page 11)
  - 'Dialogue rules' (Page 13)
  - 'Path of ideas' (Page 33)

- Pupils proofread and edit the middle of their story. They write the revised version onto the worksheet—using the back of the sheet if necessary.

Additional activities

- Pupils use the checklist on the worksheet to edit other pieces of their writing.
- Pupils keep a dictionary of misspelt words that they can include in their weekly spelling lists.

Assessment checklist

- Did the pupil mark corrections onto his/her own first draft?
- Did the pupil use a dictionary to correct spelling errors?
- Did the pupil read his/her work aloud—either to himself/herself or to a partner?
- Did the pupil present/publish the edited version onto the worksheet?

REVISING THE MIDDLE

Revising is a very important part of writing. No-one can write a perfect story on the first draft! You will now look for mistakes and ways to improve your story.

1. Reread the middle of your story.

2. Edit your story.

   (a) Circle words that you think are misspelt. Use a dictionary to check them and write the correct spelling.

   (b) Add in any missing punctuation. Look for missing full stops, capital letters, commas and apostrophes.

   (c) Check that you have followed the rules of dialogue.

   – When a new character speaks, start a new paragraph. ☐

   – If there is a speech tag, the comma goes outside the speech marks, unless it is part of the speech. ☐

   – Include what the characters are doing and thinking. ☐

   Add your edits to your dialogue.

3. Does the middle of your story:

• continue the events from the beginning of your story?	Yes	No
• include problems for the characters to solve?	Yes	No
• let the reader know more about the characters' personalities?	Yes	No

   If you answered 'no', redraft parts of your middle.

4. Present the corrected middle of your story below.

_____

_____

_____

_____

_____

_____

_____

_____

_____

REVISING THE END

Objectives

- Experiments with strategies for proofreading his/her own writing.
- Presents a revised version of the end of his/her own story.

Teacher information

- Pupils need to have completed activity:

  'Drafting – 3: Ending a story' (page 39) prior to this activity.

- Explain to the class that they will now revise the end of their story. Revising is one of the most important stages of writing. No author writes a perfect story on the first draft.

- Pupils will need a copy of the end of their story with them ('Ending a story' – page 39). Explain to the class that they will only be revising the end of their story in this lesson. This may only be one or two paragraphs. A whole lesson has been allocated for this so pupils will have time to not only find mistakes, but to improve their story if required.

- Explain to the class what is required at each step of the worksheet. Encourage pupils to read aloud to see if their writing sounds correct. Pupils may work in pairs and ask their partner if they think their writing sounds correct and if their story is interesting. Remind pupils to make the corrections onto their draft worksheet.

- Remind pupils that they have completed activities that should help them to create an effective story ending. Pupils can look at previous activities, such as:

  - 'Effective dialogue' (Page 11)
  - 'Dialogue rules' (Page 13)
  - 'Path of ideas' (Page 34)

- Pupils proofread and edit the end of their story. They write the revised version onto the worksheet—using the back of the sheet if necessary.

Additional activities

- Pupils use the checklist on the worksheet to edit other pieces of their writing.
- Pupils keep a dictionary of misspelt words that they can include in their weekly spelling lists.

Assessment checklist

- Did the pupil mark corrections onto his/her own first draft?
- Did the pupil use a dictionary to correct spelling errors?
- Did the pupil read his/her work aloud—either to himself/herself or to a partner?
- Did the pupil present/publish the edited version onto the worksheet?

REVISING THE END

Revising is a very important part of writing. No-one can write a perfect story on the first draft! You will now look for mistakes and ways to improve your story.

1. Reread the end of your story.

2. Edit your story.

    (a) Circle words that you think are misspelt. Use a dictionary to check them and write the correct spelling.

    (b) Add in any missing punctuation. Look for missing full stops, capital letters, commas and apostrophes.

    (c) Check that you have followed the rules of dialogue.

        – When a new character speaks, start a new paragraph. ☐

        – If there is a speech tag, the comma goes outside the speech marks, unless it is part of the speech. ☐

        – Include what the characters are doing and thinking. ☐

    Add your edits to your dialogue.

3. In the end of your story:

    • do the characters solve the problems in the story? | Yes | | No |

    • have all of the questions been answered? | Yes | | No |

    If you answered 'no', redraft parts of you story ending.

4. Present the corrected ending of your story below.

_____

_____

_____

_____

_____

_____

_____

_____

_____

_____

_____

 **Presenting 1**

AUTHOR PROFILE

Objective

- Creates a short passage of writing for a specific purpose.

Preparation

- Look in the library for books that contain author profiles and have them available for the class.

Teacher information

- Ask the pupils to bring in their favourite book for this lesson.

- Identify where an author profile is found.

- Share the profiles with the class. Discuss the information contained in an author profile.

  - personal information about the author

  - information about other stories he/she has written

  - sometimes a photograph

- Ask the pupils to choose their favourite author. Brainstorm to discover information that they already know and discuss where they could find other facts.

- Use the Internet or library to research information about the authors. Show pupils how to use a search engine such as 'Google'.

- Search for authors under specific publishing houses; e.g. Penguin, Scholastic.

  A good general website for author information is:

  http://www.ukchildrensbooks.co.uk

- Pupils complete the worksheet for their chosen author.

Additional activities

- Pupils can complete a detailed research project or fact file on their author and present it to the class.

- Display the author profiles in the classroom.

Assessment checklist

- Could the pupil identify the author profile in his/her chosen story?

- Could the pupil identify the type of information found in an author profile?

- Did the pupil complete a profile for a favourite author?

An author profile is usually found on the inside back cover of a book. It contains interesting information about the author and sometimes has a photo.

1. Think of your favourite author. Find out eight to ten interesting facts about him or her and write an author profile.

   Author's name:

   _____

2. Draw or glue a picture of the author in the box.

INTRODUCING YOU

Objective

- Selects text type, subject matter and language to suit a specific audience and purpose.

Teacher information

- Encourage pupils to reread the profile they wrote on their favourite author. Revise the different types of information included in a profile.

- Explain to the pupils that they are going to create a personal author profile about themselves. Brainstorm the information that they might like to include.

  - their name
  - city/town/village where they live
  - members of their family
  - hobbies
  - stories that they have written or would like to write
  - photograph of themselves
  - genre they enjoy writing the most

- Pupils complete the worksheet individually.

- Pupils draw a picture or attach a photo of themselves in the box.

Additional activities

- In pairs, pupils swap profiles and introduce each other.
- Display completed profiles around the classroom.
- Link with information technology:
  - Present information in a program suitable for website display.
  - Alternatively, completed computer profiles could be combined into a PowerPoint™ presentation.

Assessment checklist

- Did the pupil recall the information needed in an author profile?
- Did the pupil create his/her own author profile, including this information?

1. Imagine you are a famous author! You are going to write an author profile about yourself.

   When you write your author profile, write it as if you were writing about someone else – use 'he/she' instead of 'I'. Write in the present tense and aim to include eight to ten interesting facts.

2. Add a photo or draw a picture of yourself.

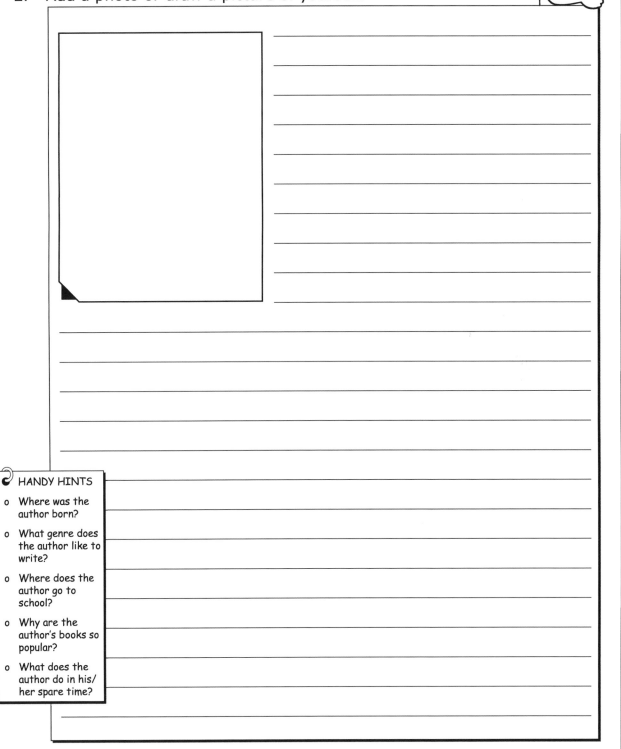

HANDY HINTS

o Where was the author born?

o What genre does the author like to write?

o Where does the author go to school?

o Why are the author's books so popular?

o What does the author do in his/her spare time?

STORY BLURBS

Objective

- Examines how writers try to engage audiences.

Teacher information

- Using a variety of novels and story books, read the blurbs from the back cover of each book to the class. Explain that a blurb is a short paragraph about the story, designed to make the reader want to buy the book. Discuss the sort of information that is included in each of the chosen blurbs, as well as the information that is left out. Which story blurb is the most effective?

  IN: characters in the story

            events from the story

            hints at the action to come

  OUT: the actual ending!

  Note: The blurb from Emily Rodda's Deltora quest series is a good example.

- Discuss the idea that some blurbs contain testimonials, which praise the story. [*Harry Potter and the chamber of secrets* by JK Rowling contains testimonials.]

- Pupils choose one story blurb, from either the provided examples or from a book of their own choice and complete the worksheet.

Additional activities

- The pupils choose a story blurb that doesn't appeal to them and rewrite it so that it sounds more interesting.

- Pupils write a testimonial for the blurb of their chosen book.

Assessment checklist

- Could the pupil identify the elements of a story blurb?

- Could the pupil nominate the most effective blurb and provide a reason for his/her choice?

- Could the pupil complete an analysis of a chosen story blurb? [Worksheet activity]

A blurb is found on the back cover of a book. It is written to make the reader want to buy the book.

1. Choose a book and read its blurb.

   Answer the following questions about the blurb.

   (a) Title of book

   (b) Author

   (c) Name the characters in the story.

   (d) What does the blurb tell you about the storyline?

   (e) Predict what you think might happen later in the story.

   (f) Does the story sound interesting to you? [Yes] [No]
   Explain why.

   (g) Would you buy this book? [Yes] [No]

   (h) Which genre does the story fit into?

INTRODUCING YOUR STORY

Objective

- Examines how writers try to engage audiences and experiments with these techniques.

Teacher information

- Review the information included in a story blurb.

- Explain to the pupils that they are each going to write a story blurb for the story they have written.

- Remind them that they are trying to convince someone to read their story. What information should they include?

  – names of characters

  – a brief summary of some of the events

  – hints at what is to come, without giving away the ending

- As a group, write a blurb for a well-known nursery rhyme or fairytale.

  Example:

  'A young girl named Goldilocks lies down to rest in a comfortable bed. Exhausted from her day's adventures, she falls asleep. The trouble is, the house is owned by three bears, who don't know that Goldilocks has sat in their chairs and eaten their porridge. What will happen when the bears return?'

- Pupils complete the worksheet for their own story. They will need to reread their story from the previous lessons and make notes about the characters, setting, plot etc.

- Pupils choose a person to read their blurb and complete the interest scale.

Additional activities

- Pupils read their blurbs aloud to the group. The class can vote on which blurb sounds the most interesting and why.

- Write a testimonial for another pupil's story. Pupils will need to read the blurb and the story to do this.

Assessment checklist

- Did the pupil participate in the creation of a group story blurb?

- Did the pupil's created story blurb contain the correct elements?

- Did the pupil ask another person to complete the scale about his/her blurb?

INTRODUCING YOUR STORY

1. Reread the story you have written.

2. Write a blurb for your story. Make it as interesting as you can—but don't give away the ending! Remember: You are trying to convince someone to read your story.

_____
_____
_____
_____
_____
_____
_____
_____

HANDY HINTS

o Retell part of your story.

o Name your characters.

o Include some information about the setting.

o Explain the problem that needs to be solved.

o You can include some exciting dialogue in the blurb.

o Don't give away the ending!

o You could leave your blurb on a 'cliffhanger' so the readers want to know more!

3. Ask one person to read your blurb. Ask that person to complete the 'blurb interest scale'.

Name: _____

Does the blurb make you want to read the story?

| 0 | 1 | 2 | 3 | 4 | 5 | 6 | 7 | 8 | 9 | 10 |

No! Not at all.　　Not fussed! May read the story.　　Yes! Can't wait to read the story.